VOL
ENUMERATION
PERSONAL ILLUMINATIONS

MY BOOK OF LISTS

JAMES C. CHRISTENSEN

PERSONAL ILLUMINATIONS

VOL. III
ENUMERATION

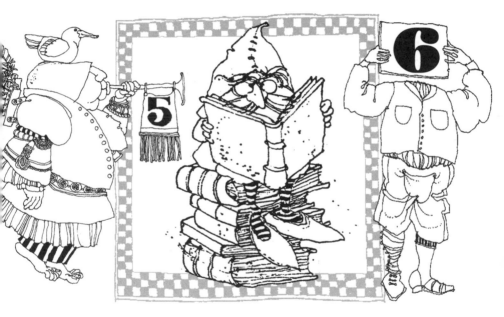

SHADOW
MOUNTAIN

Shadow Mountain is a registered trademark of Deseret Book Company. Visit us at www.shadowmountain.com

ISBN 1-57345-857-0

OTHER BOOKS IN THE PERSONAL ILLUMINATIONS SERIES:

Imagination: My Creative Journal
Exploration: My Travel Journal
Illumination: My Spiritual Journal
The Personal Illuminations Journal (hardcover)

Designed by Peter Landa and Milly Iacono
Printed in the United States of America

10   9   8   7   6   5   4   3   2   1

INTROOUCTION

J A M E S   C.   C H R I S T E N S E N

Welcome to your book of lists. Here's the place to keep track of everything from the mundane to the sacred, from home improvement plans to personal goals for the year.

If you're like me, there's *no end* to the lists, so why not start this book in the middle? There's no right or wrong order. Sometimes the movies you want to remember sit in your brain right next to the thank-you notes you need to write and memories from the best days of the past year.

In this book you'll find the basic lists front and center...and at the end, too! But you might be caught up short by some of the lists, like a list of things you're afraid to try.

This is your book. You don't have to share it with anyone, and you get all the pleasure of checking things off your lists when you're finished. When it's all filled up, you can put it on a shelf and start a new one.

MUSIC TO FIND:

MUSIC TO TRY:

___ BLUES

___ EUROPEAN POP

___ JAZZ

___ CHORAL

___ ORCHESTRAL

___ RHYTHM AND BLUES

___ ROCK AND ROLL

___ PUNK ROCK

___ HEAVY METAL

___ CHAMBER MUSIC

___ RAP

___ SWING

___ TECHNO POP

___ FUNK

BOOKS TO READ:

MOVIES TO SEE:

MY FAVORITE MOVIES:

MY MOVIE AWARDS:

COMEDY:

DRAMA:

ACTION:

DOCUMENTARY:

SCIENCE FICTION:

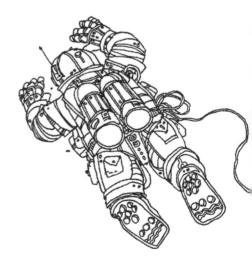

THINGS TO DO WITH MY FAMILY:

NOW:

LATER:

WHILE I STILL CAN:

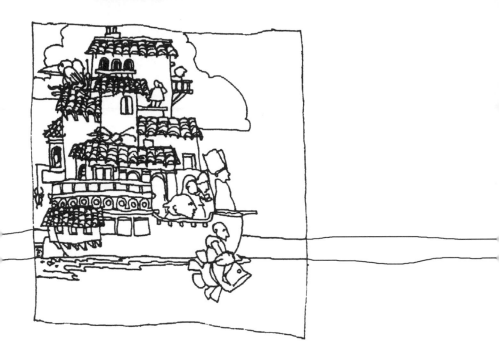

WHILE THEY'RE STILL YOUNG:

THINGS AND PLACES I WOULD LIKE TO SEE BEFORE I DIE:

CUENCA

This is my best trip to CUENCA. hiked up to the castle at the top, DID a couple of nice Pencil drawings. The weather is great. I continue to be fascinated with the way these buildings merge with the stone of the mountains. after a few hundred years it is hard to see what is the mountains & what is man made.

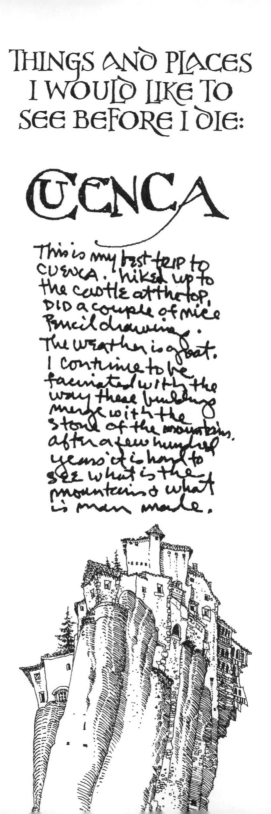

RANDOM ACTS OF KINDNESS...
I HAVE DONE FOR OTHER PEOPLE:

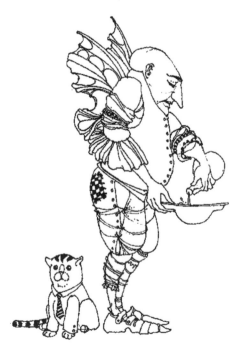

PEOPLE HAVE DONE FOR ME:

GREAT GIFT IDEAS FOR FAMILY, FRIENDS, AND COLLEAGUES:

GIFT IDEAS FOR ME:

THANK-YOU NOTES TO WRITE:

GUESTS TO INVITE FOR DINNER:

HOME IMPROVEMENTS:

SMALL REPAIRS:

FIVE THINGS TO ACCOMPLISH THIS YEAR:

LIST OF THINGS I WANT TO FORGET: IT'S OK TO LEAVE THIS PAGE BLANK.

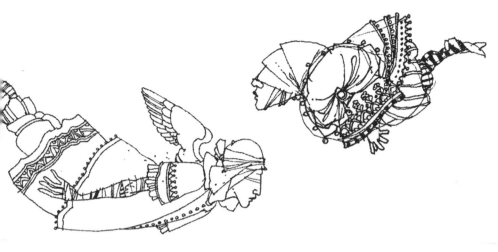

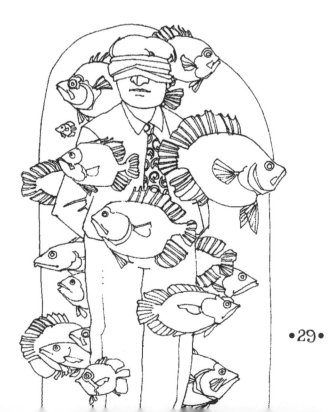

FRIENDS TO KEEP IN TOUCH WITH:

PEOPLE I WANT TO FIND AGAIN:

THINGS I'M AFRAID TO TRY:

THINGS I'M GOING TO TRY ANYWAY:

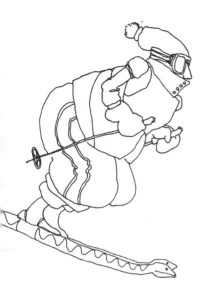

TEN GREAT DAYS THIS YEAR:

WAYS I CAN BE NICE TO NATURE:

PEOPLE I ADMIRE
MY HEROES AND ROLE MODELS:

MURPHY'S LAW: EVERYTHING THAT CAN GO WRONG WILL GO WRONG. WHAT'S GONE WRONG LATELY?

MURPHY LIVES

BRIDGES TO MEND:

DEBTS I OWE:

BRAVEST THINGS I'VE DONE:

FAVORITE QUOTATIONS:

Things I Want To Learn:

REALLY HARD THINGS THAT ARE WORTH DOING:

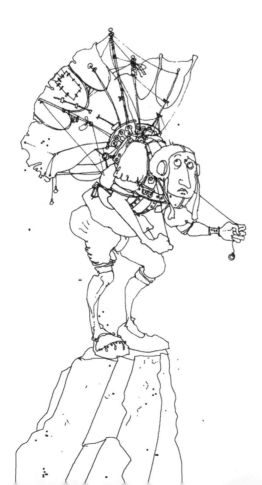

GOALS TO STRIVE FOR AT WORK:

HEALTH LIST:
- ANNUAL CHECKUPS SCHEDULED:

- WHAT I DO TO GET IN SHAPE:

- WHAT I DO TO STAY IN SHAPE:

FIVE MOST IMPORTANT POSSESSIONS:

GOOD. NOW CONSIDER THE NEXT LIST...

FIVE MOST IMPORTANT THINGS YOU POSSESS:

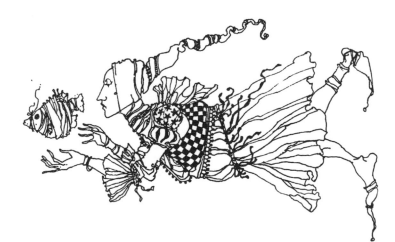

ANY DIFFERENCES BETWEEN THE TWO?

GREAT STORIES:

EMBARRASSING MOMENTS:

HUMBLING EXPERIENCES:

RESTAURANTS TO TRY
AND WHAT I'VE HEARD ABOUT THEM:

Ye Olde
Ethelbert's
Chew &
Choke

CUISINES TO TRY:

___ THAI

___ CREOLE

___ INDIAN

___ ETHIOPIAN

___ BRAZILIAN

___ JAPANESE

___ MEXICAN

___ MANDARIN

___ KOREAN

___ VIETNAMESE

___ ARGENTINE

___ FRENCH

___ ITALIAN

___ OTHER

MY FAVORITE FOODS:

FAVORITE SCRIPTURES:

WHY I AM A SUPERIOR BEING:

AND OTHER REASONS I AM A WORTHY PERSON

A PAGE TO VENT:

...NOW MOVE ON

DAYDREAMS:

FAVORITE PETS I HAVE KNOWN:

PETS I'D LIKE TO HAVE ONE DAY:

GREAT IDEAS AT THE TIME...

SOMETIMES THE BEST SOLUTIONS COME
FROM GOOFY IDEAS.

TIME CAPSULE:

A LETTER WRITTEN TO MYSELF TO BE READ IN ONE YEAR (OR FIVE). HOW AM I DOING? WHAT AM I DOING NOW TO ACHIEVE MY GOALS?

TIME CAPSULE (CONTINUED)

INDEX